BABY STAR
The Christmas Goat

Written by Kerry Skidmore
Illustrated by Julie Skidmore

ISBN: 9781796597899
Ministry Resource Publishing

Dedicated to all the "kids"
who love Christmas!

It was a quiet but cold night in the pasture around Bethlehem. The sheep were settling down to sleep, and the goat herd was doing the same.

All the baby animals were nestling by their mothers, all except Baby Star.

She was a tiny little goat when she was born, and the mother goat wasn't able to feed her and take care of her.

The shepherds named her "Star" because she had a little star right in the middle of her little brown forehead.

The kind shepherds took her in and fed her milk until she was able to eat grain and grass.

On nights like this, Star got pretty cold. She tried to get near the other goats to get warm, but they shooed her away. She finally found a place near the shepherds and began to close her eyes.

Just then, there was a huge light in the sky. A bright star was shining. It had been very dark but now the sky was bright as day.

And up in the sky there were angel voices singing beautiful, glorious songs.

Then an angel began to speak to the shepherds.

The angel told them that a little baby had been born in the stable in Bethlehem. He said they should go see this special baby. He was not just any baby—it was Baby Jesus! God's own Son!

The shepherds were amazed, excited but scared. They didn't know what to think of it all. But they decided they had to go see this baby!

They made sure their flocks were enclosed and protected, then they gathered their coats around them and prepared to go to Bethlehem.

They started off, but Baby Star got up to go with them. She had been sleeping right by the shepherds and when they got up, she got up too.

"No, Star, you go back! You can't come!" shouted the shepherds. Star was startled by all the yelling, but something inside her made her determine that wherever they were going, she was going too!

The shepherds walked fast, but so did Baby Star. Her little legs had to run to keep up, but keep up she did. Finally they gave up trying to send her back to the flocks and herds, and just let her follow them.

When they finally got to Bethlehem, the star that had been shining so bright in the sky led them right to the stable the angel had told them about.

Sure enough, there in the manger, lay a wonderful, beautiful child. His mother and father were watching over Him and they welcomed the shepherds who came to visit.

When the shepherds saw the baby, they bowed down in worship. They were speechless at this great event, the birth of this marvelous Child.

But not Baby Star! She walked right up to the baby, and began to lick His little hand. Baby Jesus looked at her, and when He saw her funny face, her little horns and the little star right in the middle of her little brown forehead, He began to smile and laugh! He reached out and patted Baby Star on her head.

The baby's mother, Mary, thought she better get the little baby goat away from her child, but then she saw how delighted He was to see this funny little goat with a little star like the great big star in the sky.

Mary welcomed Baby Star and offered her some hay that was by the manger.

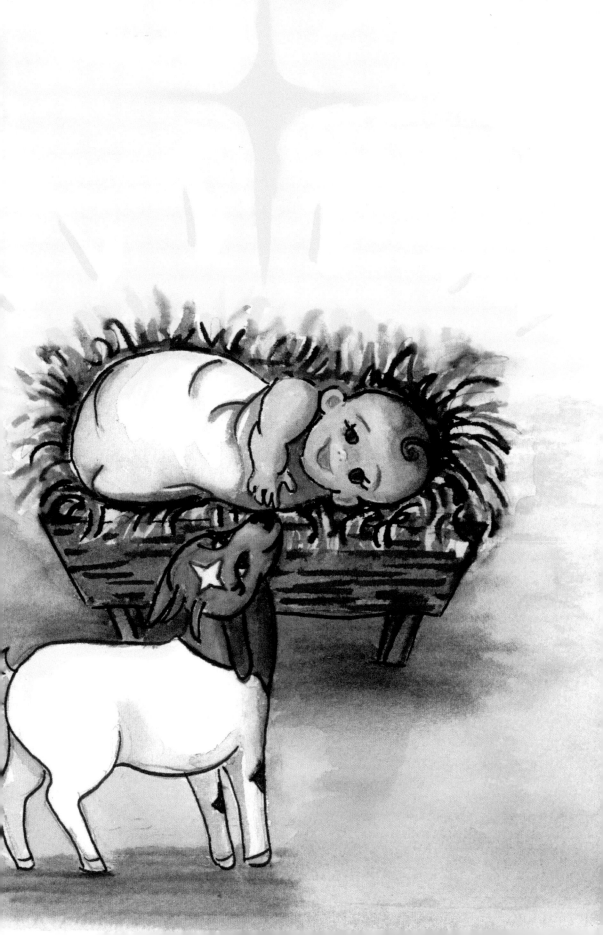

Joseph too welcomed Baby Star, and let her settle down by him to munch on her hay. The shepherds were amazed that this little goat who was such a nuisance had become such a hit on this wonderful night.

Soon it was time for the shepherds to leave and go back to their flocks and herds. Baby Star got up to go with them, and Baby Jesus waived his little hands at her as she left.

From that time on, Baby Star was the prize of the shepherds. The other goats knew not to butt her or push her around because the shepherds were quick to defend her.

When they settled down to sleep on a cold night, Baby Star lay right in the middle of the herd while all the others circled around her to keep her warm.

Baby Star had been touched by this special Baby, and she became special too.

And so it was with the shepherds themselves. They told everybody they met about Baby Jesus, the Son of God, who was born in Bethlehem.

He had come to bring God's peace and love to everyone as He brought it to them that special night.

Today we are all special when we come to know how much God loves us and we learn to love Him too.

This Christmas Baby Jesus can be born in your heart and you will always be in the middle of His love and care.

"If you have enjoyed this little book
please write a 5-Star Review
on Amazon.com.

It really helps me and others
who might like this book.

Made in the USA
Middletown, DE
01 November 2020